This Bing book belongs to:

....

Bing™ Annual 2024

Copyright © 2023 Acamar Films Ltd

The *Bing* television series is created by Acamar Films and Brown Bag Films and adapted from the original books by Ted Dewan.

Hiding (pp.14–21) is based on the original story written by Gerard Foster, Lucy Murphy, Mikael Shields and An Vrombaut.
Skateboard (pp.30–37) is based on the original story written by Lucy Murphy, Mikael Shields, Ted Dewan and Philip Bergkvist.
Fireworks (pp.50–57) is based on the original story written by Susan Earl, Lucy Murphy, Mikael Shields, Philip Bergkvist and Ted Dewan. *Fireworks* was adapted from the original story by Rebecca Gerlings and abridged by Lauren Holowaty.

10 9 8 7 6 5 4 3 2 1

ISBN: 978-0-00-855705-8

First published in the United Kingdom by HarperCollins *Children's Books* in 2023
HarperCollins *Children's Books* is a division of HarperCollins*Publishers* Ltd
1 London Bridge Street
London SE1 9GF

www.harpercollins.co.uk

HarperCollins*Publishers*
Macken House, 39/40 Mayor Street Upper
Dublin 1, D01 C9W8, Ireland

Written by Lauren Holowaty

Printed by Oriental Press in Dubai

MIX
Paper | Supporting responsible forestry
FSC™ C007454
www.fsc.org

This book is produced from independently certified FSC™ paper to ensure responsible forest management.

For more information visit: www.harpercollins.co.uk/green

Contents

Christmas Wishes

Read about Bing's favourite Christmas things!

Name: Bing

Favourite Christmas food:

Amma's Christmas carroty bake

and banana trifle

Favourite Christmas present:

A Hoppity Voosh Rocket Sledge

Christmas wish: For it to snow!

Your turn!

My name:

My favourite Christmas food:

My favourite Christmas present:

My Christmas wish:

Present Patterns

Look at the colourful presents Bing and friends want to give to each other. What present comes next in each row?

Which present is your favourite?

Christmas Colouring

Can you use your brightest pencils to colour in this festive picture of Bing, Pando and Sula?

Happy Christmas!

Merry I-Spy

Look at these pictures from
Bing's Christmas and play I-spy!

1 'p' is for

p _ _ _ _ _ _

2 't' is for

t _ _ _

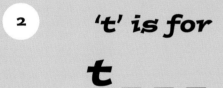

3 'h' is for

h _ _

4 's' is for

s _ _ _ _ _

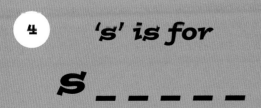

Answers: 1. present, 2. tree, 3. hat, 4. sledge

Bing's Festive Paper Chains

Bing is helping Flop decorate for Christmas. You can help too. Ask a grown-up to cut up the strips of paper and follow the simple instructions to make your own paper chains!

You will need:

- A grown-up to help you
- Scissors
- The Bing patterned paper (opposite)
- Sheets of coloured A4 paper (to make longer chains)
- Sticky tape

What to do:

1 Carefully cut out the strips of paper opposite.

2 Cut the extra paper into strips of the same length if you are making longer chains.

3 Curl one strip of paper into a hoop shape and secure it with sticky tape as shown.

4 Loop the next paper strip through the first hoop and make another hoop, securing it again with sticky tape.

5 Keep looping the hoops together until you have the chain length you need, and then hang up your Christmassy chains to decorate!

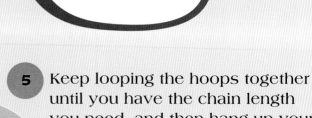

The Perfect Playhouse

Can you make the perfect playhouse for Bing with your favourite colours?

What would you put in Bing's playhouse?

Hiding

Round the corner,
not far away,
Bing is **playing**
with Flop today . . .

"I'm hiding!" calls Bing, giggling behind a tree in the park. "Come and find me!"

Flop looks around.

"BOO!" says Bing, jumping out from behind the tree.

"Oh, Bing!" gasps Flop.

"I booed you, Flop," says Bing.

"Yes, so you did," agrees Flop.

Bing runs off to hide again.

"Oh, where's he gone?" says Flop. Just then, he hears a noise.

"Hmm. These bushes are very giggly," remarks Flop.

Bing jumps out from behind the bush . . .

"BOO!"

"Oh!" says Flop, surprised. "It was YOU, Bing!"

After all that hiding, Bing is hungry.

"Shall we find some fruit for a **BIG** fruit salad?" suggests Flop.

"Yes! Let's go to Padget's shop!" cheers Bing. "Can we have apples and pears and oranges and . . . a **whole pineapple**, Flop?"

"We can," says Flop, as they walk together.

In Padget's shop, Flop gets a basket for the fruit and Bing runs behind a shelf.

"I'm **hiding!**" Bing calls. "Come and **find** me!"

"Oh, where's Bing gone?" says Flop. He starts to look around . . .

Bing moves around the shop hiding from Flop. Suddenly Flop jumps in front of Bing.

"BOO! Found you!" says Flop.

Bing laughs. He loves playing hiding!

Bing accidentally drops some oranges. One rolls towards the storeroom door . . .

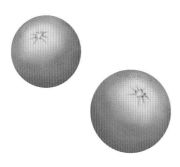

It's the perfect hiding place! Bing goes inside and shuts the door.

"I'm hiding!"

calls Bing from inside the storeroom. "Come and find me, Flop!"

But Padget and Flop are still picking up the oranges. They don't hear Bing through the closed door.

"Now, what else was it you wanted, Flop?" asks Padget.

"Apparently we need a whole pineapple," says Flop.

"Oh yes," says Padget. "I know I've got a pineapple somewhere."

Bing tries to open the storeroom door. He twists the handle, but it doesn't seem to work.

"Hmmpf! FLOP!" shouts Bing.

"I'M STILL HIDING!"

He feels a little worried.

Flop looks around the shop for Bing, but he can't see him. Then he hears Bing calling.

"Coming, Bing!" says Flop, heading to the storeroom.

Flop opens the door.

"There you are, Bing."

"Flop!" says Bing, running towards him for a hug.

"Are you okay?" asks Flop.

"I was scared," says Bing. "I couldn't see you. I was hiding and I couldn't open the door. You didn't come and find me, Flop."

"I didn't know you were hiding, Bing," explains Flop.

"I don't want to hide any more," says Bing.

"How about we go home for a **BIG** fruit salad?" says Flop. He takes the basket of fruit to the shop counter.

"Oh, we still haven't found a pineapple," says Padget. "Maybe they are in the storeroom. . ."

Padget, Flop and Bing head to the storeroom.

"Now, I wonder where I put them," says Padget.

"There!" cheers Bing, pointing at the pineapples.

"They were hiding too," chuckles Padget.

"Yup, and we found them!" says Bing.

"Good for you, Bing Bunny," says Flop.

Hiding . . . it's a **Bing thing.**

Hiding Story Quiz

Can you remember what happened in the story?
See if you can answer these questions.

1 What did Bing hide behind in the park? Point to the right answer.

A
B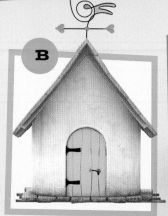
C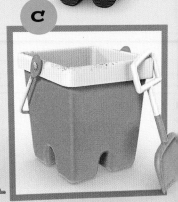

2 Who did Bing play hide-and-seek with? Colour in the right answer.

A
B
C

3 What did Bing want to buy from the shop? Trace a tick next to the right answer.

A
B
C

4 Who is the owner of the shop? Draw a circle round the right answer.

A
B
C

Answers: 1. A, 2. C, 3. A, 4. B

Who's Hiding?

Bing's friends like hiding too! Draw lines to where everyone is hiding.

1

A

2

B

3

C

4

D

Do you like playing hide-and-seek? Where's your favourite hiding place?

Peek-a-boo Pineapples

Help Bing spot all the pineapples in Padget's shop.

How many did you count altogether?

Rainybow Painting

Follow the simple instructions to make a
beautiful rainybow painting with Sula and Bing!

You will need:

- A grown-up to help you
- A pencil
- A large piece of white paper
- Paints
- A paintbrush

What to do:

1 Fold your piece of paper in half, and then unfold it and lay it flat.

2 Use your paints to paint half a rainbow. Stop at the crease.

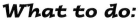

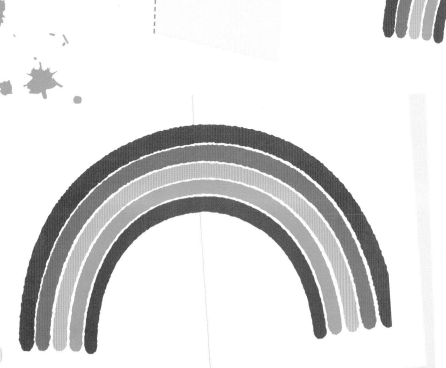

3 While the paint is wet, carefully fold the paper back in half, then press it down so that the paint transfers on to the other side.

4 Open out your paper to discover your beautiful rainybow!

Round We Go!

Play this fun game and colour in Bing and his friends along the way.

Player 1's Colouring Card

Bing

Pando

Sula

Coco

Flop

Charlie

What to do:

1. Find a friend to play with, and then choose a colouring card each

2. Take it in turns to roll a dice and move round the circle

START ▶

Bing

Pando

Sula

Coco

Flop

Charlie

3. If you land on Bing or one of his friends, colour them in on your player card

4. Keep moving round the board until you have coloured everyone in!

5. The first player to colour everyone in wins!

Skateboard

Round the corner, not far away,
Bing wants to go **fast** today . . .

"Come on, Flop," says Bing, running around the park. "Let's go **really** fast!"

"**NEEEEEEEOWWWW!**"

Pando comes zooming after Bing on his skateboard.

"**BIIIIIIING!**"

"Wow, Pando!" says Bing. "You've got a skateboard. Can I have a turn?"

"Okay," says Pando. "I'll show you how to do it first."

"Flop!" says Bing. "Pando says I can have a go on his skateboard. I'm going to go **SUPER FAST!**"

"Well, let's see how Pando does it first," says Flop.

"I know how to do it," says Bing. "You go . . .

"**NEEEEEEEEOWWWW!**"

"You may need to go slowly at first," explains Padget. "Skateboarding can be a tricky thing."

Pando shows Bing how to balance on the skateboard.

"You bend your knees and hold your arms out and push!"

Bing copies Pando's movements while Pando skates along the path.

Padget gives Bing Pando's helmet, elbow pads and kneepads so he can have a turn.

"All ready in there, Bing?" asks Flop.

"Yup!" says Bing.

As Bing steps on to the
skateboard it starts to wobble
and rolls away from him!

"Oop, careful," says Flop.

Bing tries again, but the
skateboard rolls away again.

"It won't let me get on, Flop,"
says Bing.

"Perhaps Pando can help?" suggests Flop.

Pando shows Bing how to step on to the skateboard.
"Do your foot like this, Bing," he says, carefully
stepping on.

Bing carefully steps back on to the skateboard.

"Woah! Oooh."

It's still a bit wobbly, but Flop and Pando hold Bing's hands to help him balance.

"Slowly does it," says Padget.

Bing stands on the skateboard but it doesn't go anywhere.

"You have to push, Bing," explains Padget.

"Use your back foot," adds Pando.

"Bend . . . arms . . . push," remembers Bing.

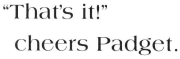

"That's it!" cheers Padget.

"Did you see, Flop?" says Bing proudly. **"I made it go!"**

"Yes, I saw," says Flop.

"Go on, Bing," cheers Pando.
"Now you can go faster."

"Bend . . . arms . . . push,"

says Bing as he starts
to skate faster . . .
and faster . . .
and even faster
down a hill.

"Ooooh, too
fast, too fast!"

says Bing, as he
wobbles . . .

Bing can't control the skateboard. He's going too fast! It hits the edge of the path and Bing falls over . . .

"Are you all right, Bing?" asks Flop.

BUMP!

"It went too fast," says Bing. "I didn't like it!"

"Oh, poor Bing," says Padget.

"Are your knees okay, Bing?" asks Flop.

"Yup," says Bing.

"Arm okay?"

"Yup," says Bing. "It's a bit ouchy."

"Wooo-ooo-woo-ooo-woo-ooh!"

"Emergency!" says Pando, bringing the skateboard back to Bing. "Come on, Bing. Get in the ambulance!"

"The ambulance won't go too fast," Padget tells Bing.

"Hmm, okay," says Bing.

Pando pushes Bing along on the skateboard ambulance.

"Wooo-ooo-woo-ooo-woo-ooh!"

He tells Bing about all the times he has fallen off his skateboard.

Flop, Padget and Pando all reassure Bing that he can try skateboarding again.

"It won't go so fast here where it's flat," says Flop.

"Okay," says Bing, getting back on to the skateboard. "Bend . . . arms . . . push. I'm doing it, Flop!"

"Good for you, Bing Bunny!" says Flop.

"NEEEEEEEOWWWW!"

Skateboarding . . . it's a **Bing** thing.

Skateboard Story Quiz

Think back to the story.
What can you remember about it?

1 **What** did Pando bring to the park? Draw a circle round the right picture.

A    **B** **C**

2 **What** did Padget give Bing to wear? Colour in the star next to the right thing.

A    **B**    **C**

3 **What** did Pando tell Bing to do? Tick the right answer.

A "Bend . . . arms . . . push!"   **B** "Go really really fast!"   **C** "Jump up and down three times."

4 **Where** does the story take place? Trace the letters of the right answer.

A 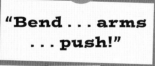 shop

C house

B  park

Answers: 1. A, 2. C, 3. A, 4. B

Things That Go, Go, Go!

Skateboards have wheels to make them go. What other things have wheels? Colour a circle next to each thing with wheels, then trace the wheel shape in the middle of the page.

Copy Bing

Bing likes to move! Can you copy all of his actions?

1

Touch your nose!

2

Reach up high!

3

Balance on one leg!

4

Turn around with a jump!

5

Jump forward and stretch!

All done? Good for you!

Happy Halloween

Bing and his friends are all dressed up for Halloween!
Can you spot which two pictures are
exactly the same?

**What do you like
to dress up as?**

Answer: 1 and 4 match.

Fire Engine Fun

Bing and his friends are excited to see a fire engine in the park! Can you look closely at the picture and answer all the questions?

1. What are the two main colours on the fire engine?

2. How many firefighters are there?

3. Which friend is sitting inside the fire engine?

4. How many petals are on this flower?

43

5. How many firefighters are wearing glasses?

6. What sound does a fire engine make?

Answers: 1. Red and yellow, 2. Four firefighters, 3. Pando, 4. There are five petals, 5. One firefighter is wearing glasses, 6. Nee-naw! Nee-naw!

Treasure Hunt

Bing is going on a treasure hunt! Use your finger or pencil to follow the trail to find the crown! How many rooms does he search?

Answer: Bing searches four rooms.

Musical Statues

Bing loves playing musical statues! Use the numbers to help you colour in the picture.

Who do you think will wobble first?

1. Black
2. Pink
3. Brown
4. Blue
5. Green
6. Orange
7. Red

Happy Birthday, Bing!

Everyone loves singing the 'Happy Birthday' song to Bing! Look closely at these two photos. Can you spot the eight differences between them?

1

2

Colour in a cake when you find each difference.

Answers: 1. A pink balloon has appeared. 2. The red balloon is now yellow. 3. Amma has gone. 4. Coco has appeared. 5. A present has appeared. 6. Sula has a crown. 7. Bing is blowing his candles out. 8. Pand is jumping up in the air.

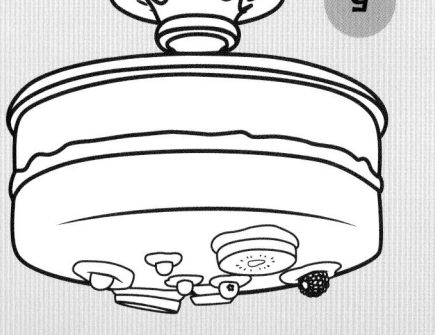

Let's Pretend Game

Play this fun Bing pretending game with a friend!

You will need:

- A friend to play with
- Two different-coloured crayons – one for each player

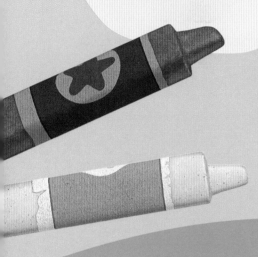

toothbrushing

swimming

What to do:

1. Find a friend and take it in turns to choose an action: swimming, toothbrushing, dancing, painting or driving. Don't tell your friend which one you have chosen.

2. Act out your action without saying what it is. Can your friend guess which one you are doing? If they can, colour in a star next to the activity with your crayon. Now it's your friend's turn to

Which activity is the most fun to act out?

painting

dancing

driving

3 choose an action. If you guess what it is, then they can colour in the star with their crayon.

4 Try acting out all the activities and see if you can both colour in all the stars!

49

Fireworks

Round the corner,
not far away,
Bing's waiting for
fireworks
today . . .

"Flop! Flop!" gasps Bing. "I see one! I see a firework!"

"Ooo! Where?" says Flop, putting down a hot oven tray and rushing to the window.

Bing points to a red light in the night sky. "There! It's **not** a very big firework . . ."

Flop follows Bing's finger. "Oh, that's because it's an aeroplane," he explains.

"It is! It's **an aeroplane!**" exclaims Bing.

"NEEEEEEEOWWWW! NEEEEEEEOWWWW!"

He stretches his arms out wide and flies around the room.

51

Ding-dong!

It's Sula and Amma at the door. Sula is wearing some pink fluffy earmuffs.

"HELLO, BING, IT'S ME!" shouts Sula.

"Hi, Sula!" replies Bing.

"HELLO, BING, IT'S ME!" Sula says again. "My earmuffles are making everything quiet!" she shouts.

"Everything except for Sula!" chuckles Amma. "Tell Bing why you're wearing them, Sula."

Sula puts the earmuffs on Bing. "I don't like noisy fireworks," she explains. "My earmuffles make them quiet. See?"

"Oh!" says Bing. "I like these!"

Suddenly there are popping and crackling noises outside. Sula quickly grabs her earmuffs back.

Bright, sparkly fireworks light up the dark sky.

WHOOOOOSH! BANG!

"Ooo!" everyone gasps, their noses pressed to the window. "Ahhh!"

"Look, Bing," says Flop. "That might be a super-bangy rocket. Over there, above the trees."

"Where? I can't see it!" says Bing, trying to spot it. "Let's go outside!"

Bing reaches for the door handle, but Sula stops him.

"Don't open the door, Bing!" she warns. "You'll let the loud in! It's too scary and you haven't got earmuffles."

"But I want to see the rockets!" explains Bing. "And I'm not scared!"

"I'm staying in here where it's quiet," says Sula, as Bing and Flop go outside.

"Good idea!" says Amma.

"Ooo!" gasps Bing, gazing up at the night sky. It's full of colourful, glittering fireworks!

Suddenly there's a super-big firework . . .

BANG!

"Ooo! That was pretty loud," says Flop. "Are you okay, Bing?"

Bing thinks for a moment. "Yes . . ." he replies slowly.

Bing and Flop watch the fireworks until there are no more bangy noises. "Oh, is it all finished, Flop?" sighs Bing.

"Let's wait, Bing," suggests Flop. "There might just be another one."

Flop is right – the fireworks start again.

BANG!

"ARGHHH!" cries Bing, rushing indoors.

Bing hides under the table as he catches his breath.

Sula joins him. "What's wrong, Bing?" she asks. But Bing doesn't answer.

"There was a big bang," explains Flop, stroking Bing's arm. "He needs a little quiet."

Outside the fireworks are still popping and crackling. "Make them stop, Flop!" says Bing.

"That bunny needs some earmuffles," explains Amma.

Flop has a clever idea. He reaches up to the tabletop.

"Let's try these!" he says, holding up his **oven gloves**.

Bing leans over and Flop slips them over his ears.

"IT'S ALL GONE QUIET!"
yells Bing.

WHOOSH! POP-POP-POP! CRACKLE!

More fireworks explode outside.

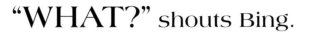

"Bing, did they work?" asks Sula.

"WHAT?" shouts Bing.

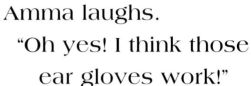

Amma laughs.
"Oh yes! I think those ear gloves work!"

Sula runs over to the window. "Wow! Bing, look!" she exclaims.

"THAT'S A SUPER-ROCKET," cheers Bing. "BUT IT'S NOT TOO LOUD!"

"Good for you, Bing bunny," chuckles Flop.

Everyone huddles together to watch the night sky.

WHOOSH! POP-POP-POP! CRACKLE!

"Oooo!" they sigh, as the sky glows with more not-too-loud fireworks.

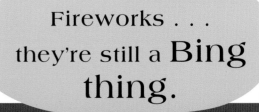

Fireworks . . . they're still a Bing thing.

Fireworks Story Quiz

What do you remember about the story?
Try this fun quiz to find out.

1 Whose house does Sula visit to watch the fireworks? Colour in the right picture.

A   B   C

2 What is Sula wearing over her ears when she arrives? Draw a circle round the right thing.

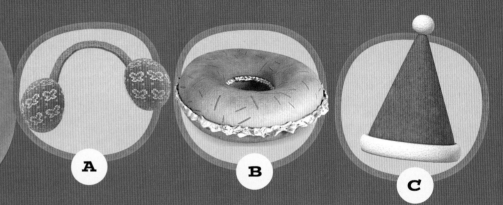

A   B   C

3 Where does Bing hide from the noisy fireworks? Finish the sentence: **Bing hides under the . . .**

A **table**

B **stairs**

C **bed**

4 What does Flop put on Bing's ears so he can't hear the noisy fireworks? Point to the right answer.

A   B   C

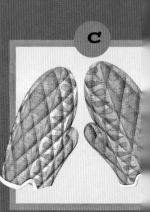

Answers: 1. B, 2. A, 3. A, 4. C

Follow the Fireworks

Can you help Bing trace the trails of these
super-bangy fireworks lighting up the sky?

How many
trails
are there
altogether?

Look at the Lights!

Can you fill the sky with colourful fireworks for Bing and his friends to enjoy? Colour them in with your brightest pencils!

60

61

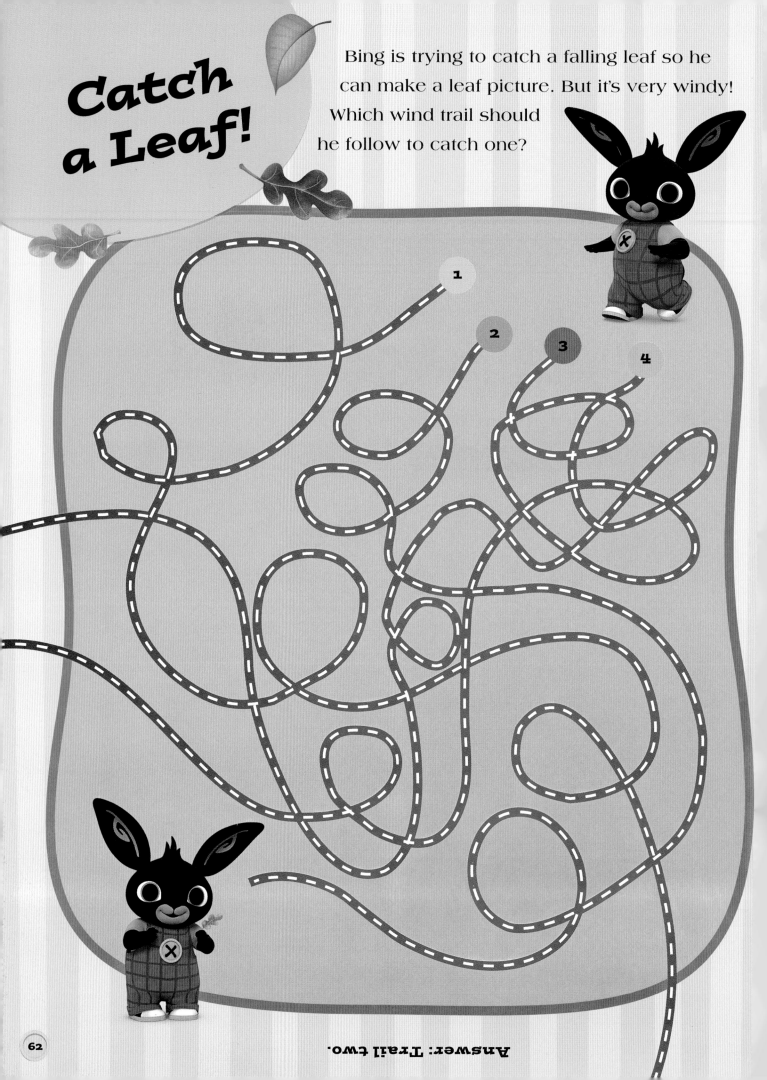

Catch a Leaf!

Bing is trying to catch a falling leaf so he can make a leaf picture. But it's very windy! Which wind trail should he follow to catch one?

1

2

3

4

Answer: Trail two.

Jigsaw Jumble

Bing loves playing in the snow with Flop. Can you see which of the jigsaw pieces below will complete the picture?

1

2

3

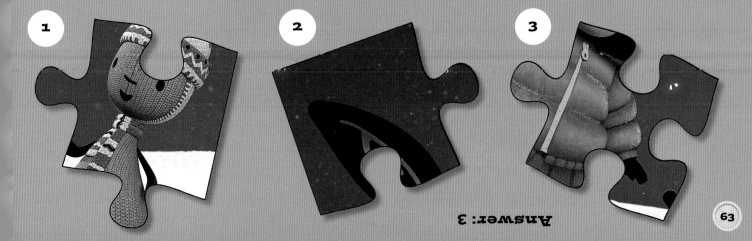

Nurse Bing

Oh dear! Hoppity isn't feeling very well.
Can you help Nurse Bing take care of him
by colouring in this picture?

Noisy Vehicles

Brrmm-brrmm! Choo-choo! Beep! Beep!

These vehicles make lots of noise!

Draw lines to match them all into pairs.

8

1

2

7

3

6

5

4

Home Time!

Bing and his friends have had a busy day playing but now it's time to go home. Trace over the dotty lines so everyone can be collected from Amma's house.

What do you
like to do when
you get home?

Night-night, Bing!

Bing has had a very exciting day. Can you help him
get ready for bed by colouring in the picture
and then saying, "Night-night, Bing!"?

Sweet
dreams!

There's a Bing book for everyone! From storybooks to moving tab books, and activity books to noisy sound books. Which one's your favourite?

ALSO AVAILABLE!

Bing Sparkle MAGIC
As seen on TV

Bing Stuckie Duckie BALLOON
As seen on TV

Bing Ready to PLAY?
A Push, Pull and Spin Book!

Bing Shake Ding BANG!
A Noisy Bing Story

Bing Where's Bing?
A lift-the-flap book

Bing My Toilet Train Sticker Book
With over 75 stickers and a reward chart!
Toilet-training fun for boys and girls

Bing The Rainybow Song
Press the button sing the song

Bing Hello, Bing!
Meet Bing and his friends!